ZAPIRO

The Devil Made Me Do It

Cartoons from *Sowetan, Mail & Guardian* and *Sunday Times*

David Philip Publishers
Cape Town & Johannesburg

Acknowledgements: Thanks to my editors at the Mail & Guardian *(Philip van Niekerk, Rehana Rossouw) and at the* Sowetan *(Aggrey Klaaste, Mike Siluma, Mike Tissong, Mokone Molete, Len Maseko) and at the* Sunday Times *(Mike Robertson, Ray Hartley) and their production staff; my assistant Muneeba Petersen; my agent Debbie McClean; Marianne Thamm for more breakfast pow-wows; all at David Philip; and as always my wife Karina.*

First published 2000 in southern Africa by
David Philip Publishers (Pty) Ltd,
208 Werdmuller Centre, Claremont 7700
in association with
Karina Turok & Jonathan Shapiro

ISBN 0-86486-369-1

Cover design by Jonathan Shapiro

Printed and bound in South Africa by The Rustica Press, Old Mill Road, Ndabeni, Cape Town
D8397

For my mother Gaby who passed away
and our daughter Nina who was born in time to meet her

30 September 1999

26 September 1999

Ex-Health Minister, now Foreign Minister

30 September 1999

3 October 1999

Titleholder under pressure at the Rugby World Cup in the UK

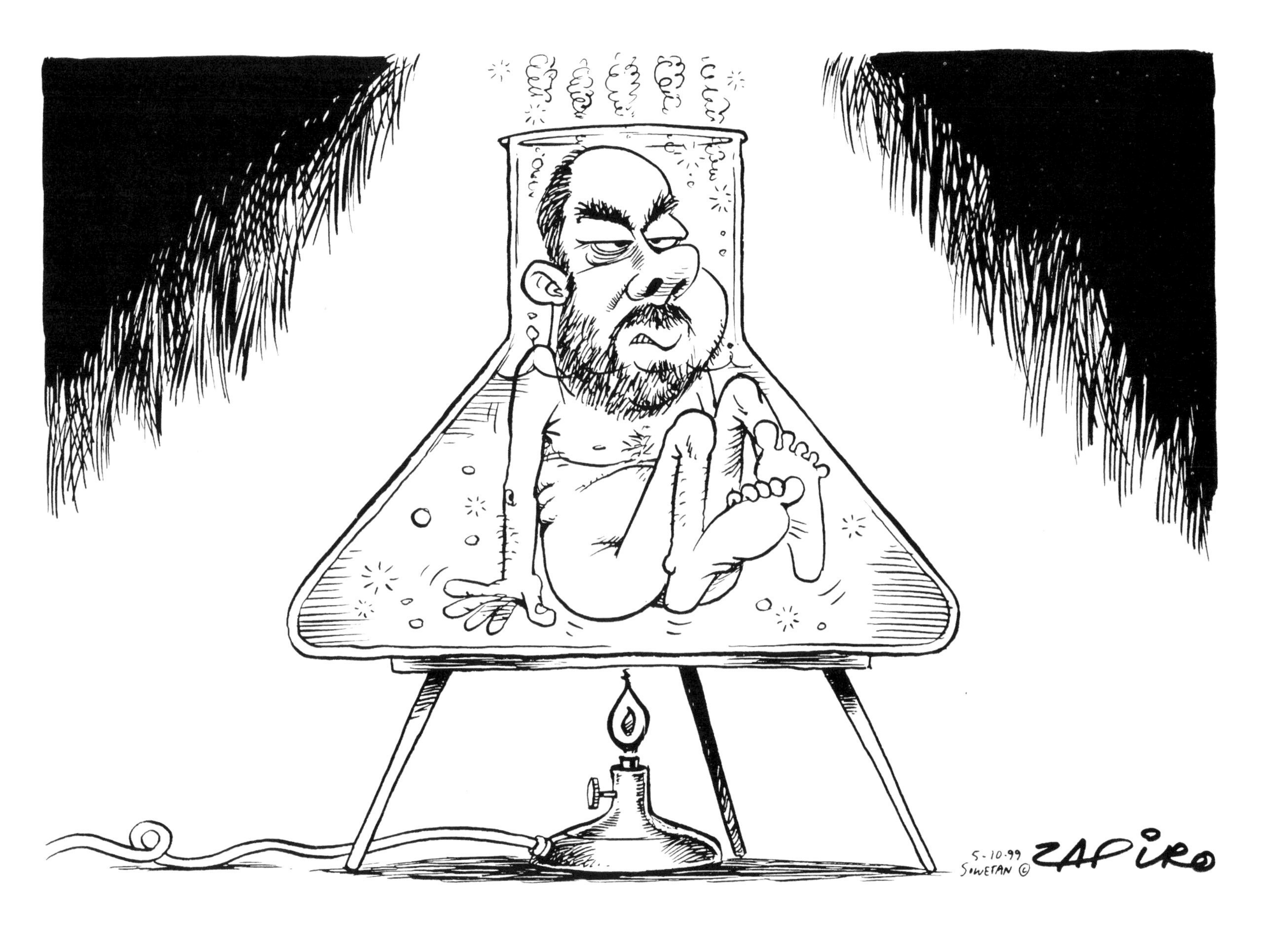

5 October 1999 Start of the trial of apartheid's chemical warfare kingpin Dr Wouter Basson

A controversial anti-rape advert is banned. After a public outcry the ban is lifted.

7 October 1999

10 October 1999

12 October 1999

Judge Hartzenberg rules that Dr Wouter Basson cannot be tried for chemically assisted atrocities in Namibia

14 October 1999

14 October 1999

Someone's coining it: dead, non-existent and ex-workers are on the payroll

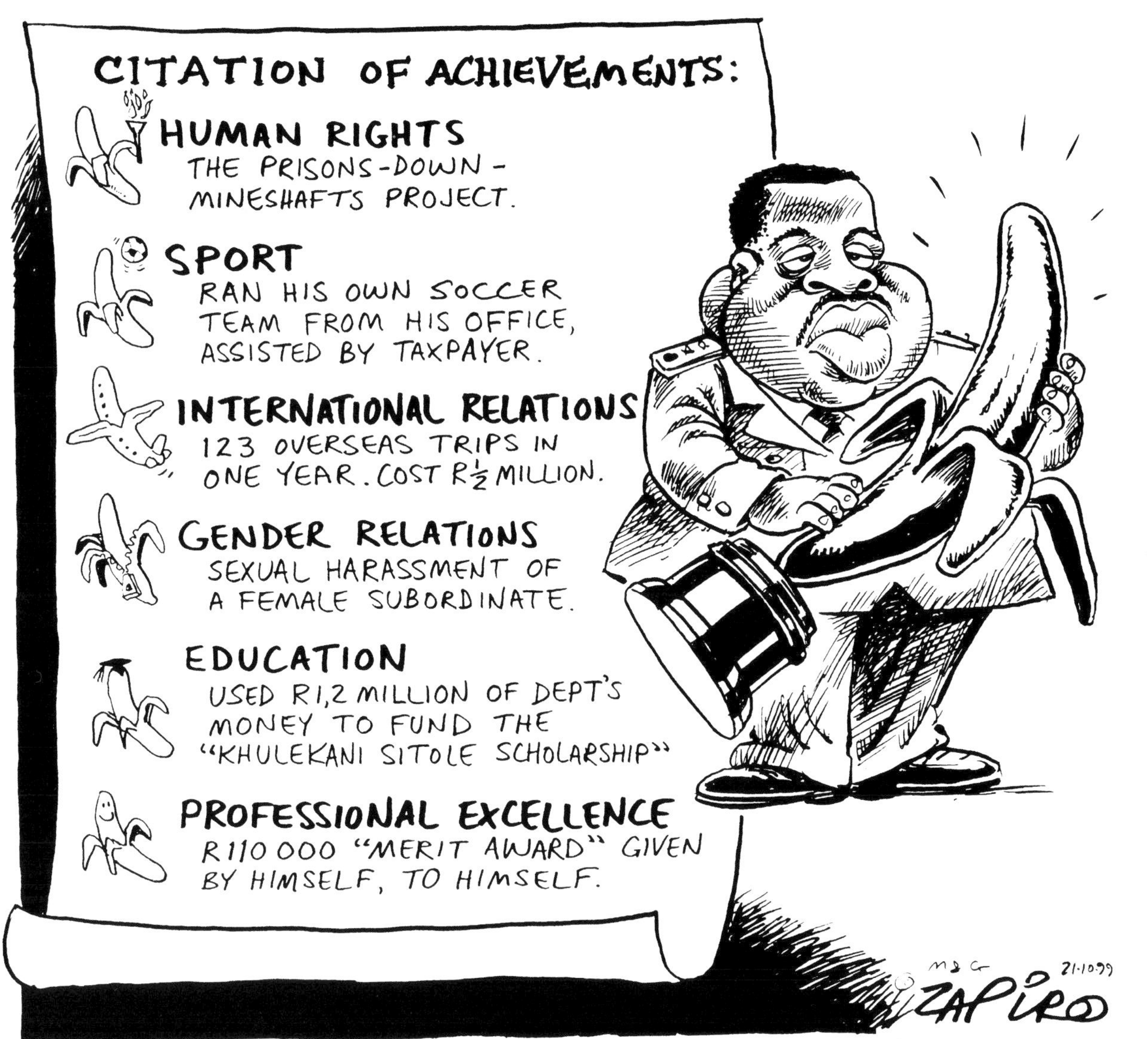

Soon-to-be-fired National Prisons Commissioner

21 October 1999

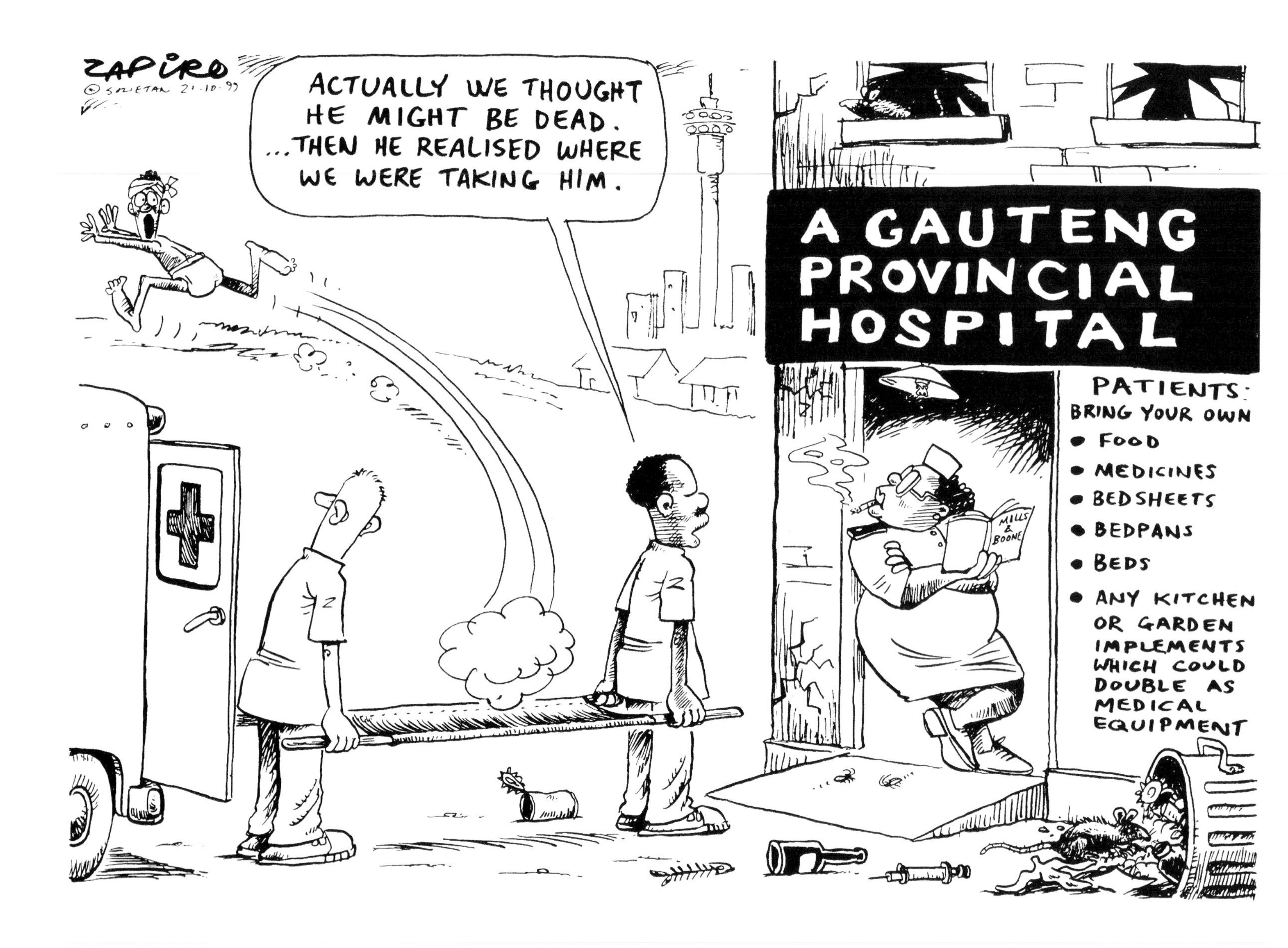

21 October 1999

22 October 1999

26 October 1999

Newly appointed National Police Commissioner

Wishful thinking. This World Cup Semi-final didn't go as planned.

28 October 1999

31 October 1999 A lenient sentence for a rapist because the victim is his daughter; the temporary banning of an anti-rape advert; and the dubious acquittal of a sports star

3 November 1999 A ruling that it's not feasible to recover the previous government's massive bank bailout

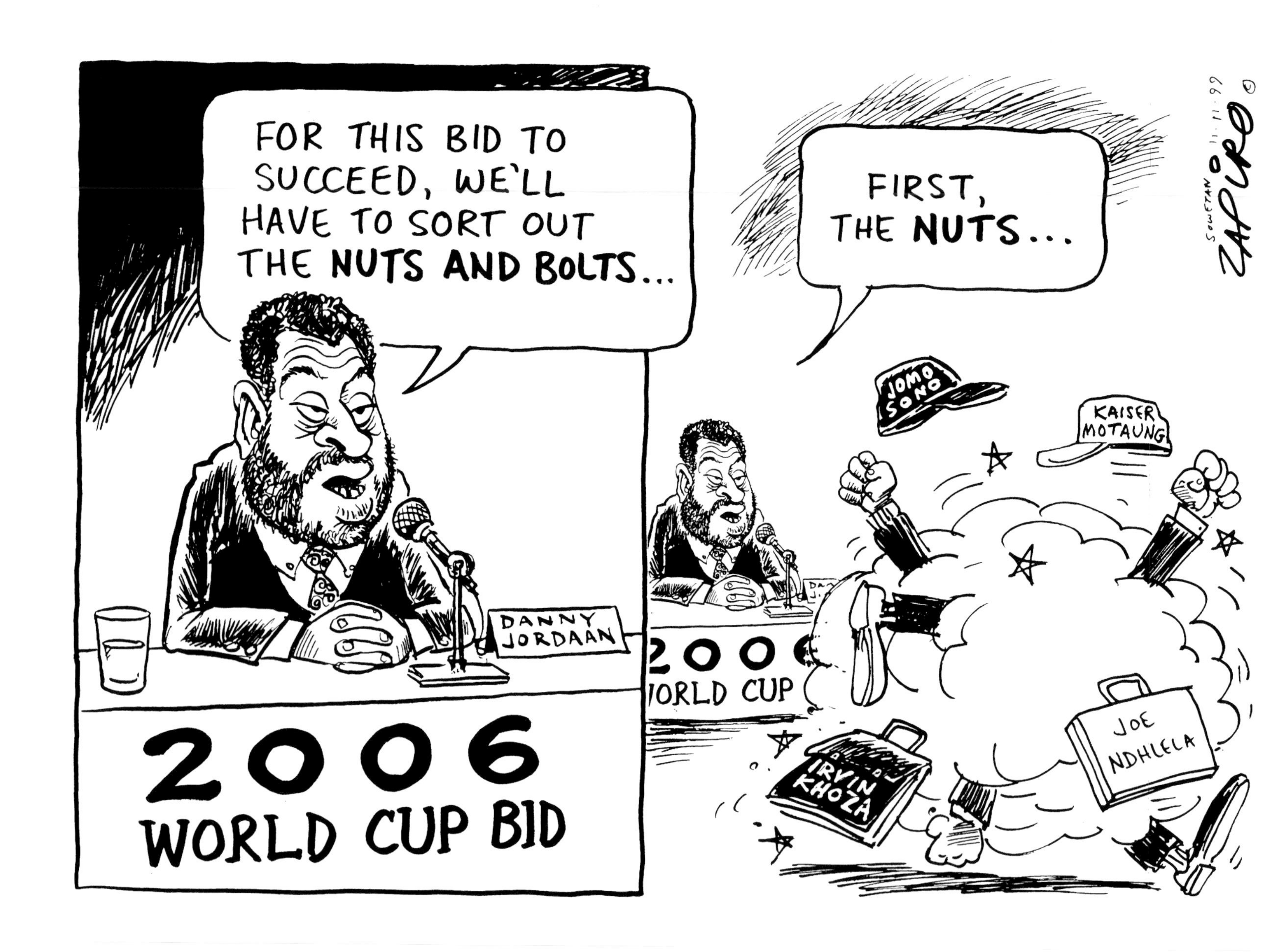

11 November 1999

Queen Elizabeth's arrival in SA is met with demands that she apologize for the Anglo-Boer War, British colonialism, King Hintsa's beheading and more

11 November 1999

14 November 1999

WHAT IS CHOGM?

Commonwealth Heads of Government Meeting

Swallowing sound at banquet for leaders of mainly poverty stricken states

The sound of human rights being endorsed by member states

The sound of human rights being applied in some of these member states

Homophobic rights abuser Bob Mugabe confronts his critics

CHOGM!

The sound of Lear Jet doors slamming as leaders say goodbye till the next summit.

SOWETAN 16.11.99 ©ZAPIRO

16 November 1999

"Editorial independence and press freedom should never ever be placed above the national interest."

— THAMI MAZWAI, BEING INTERVIEWED FOR A POSITION ON THE SABC BOARD

I ♥ BIG BROTHER

Journalists do it with a gag on

T. MAZWAI

Have you hugged your censor today?

HONK IF YOU LOVE JOE STALIN

SOWETAN 17.11.99

© ZAPIRO

17 November 1999

Playing second fiddle is Health Minister Manto Tshabalala-Msimang

18 November 1999

21 November 1999

Singin' the National Intelligence Agency Blues

Ahead of the Human Rights Commission's hearings into racism in the media, a photo published in the *Star* of a pied crow and a Marabou stork in a Ugandan rubbish tip is cited by the HRC's researcher, Claudia Braude, as a racist attempt to show the new SA in a bad light

25 November 1999

26 November 1999

28 November 1999 China sends Li Peng to prevent a meeting between President Mbeki and the visiting Dalai Lama

ZAPIRO M&G 2-12-99

AT THE WORLD PARLIAMENT OF RELIGIONS

Hosted in Cape Town

2 December 1999

7 December 1999 From unionists to environmentalists, the well-meaning protesters largely represent first-world interests

9 December 1999

12 December 1999 Finally a breakthrough: a bomb suspect's identikit is published. Turns out he's working with police. No he isn't. Yes he is. Who knows?

15 December 1999

16 December 1999

22 December 1999

29 December 1999

19 December 1999

2 January 2000

6 January 2000

9 January 2000

The cancer that caused his retirement will shortly claim his life

TERMINALLY SICK JOKES DEPT.

DON MARTIN'S LAST WORDS

The passing of another cartooning icon

13 January 2000

10 January 2000

12 January 2000

14 January 2000 After yet another mining accident

18 January 2000 Roelf Meyer resigns as deputy leader of the United Democratic Movement

New Police Commissioner calls a policewoman a 'f**king chimpanzee' and later apologizes, but a more serious case of intimidating a male officer is pending

20 January 2000

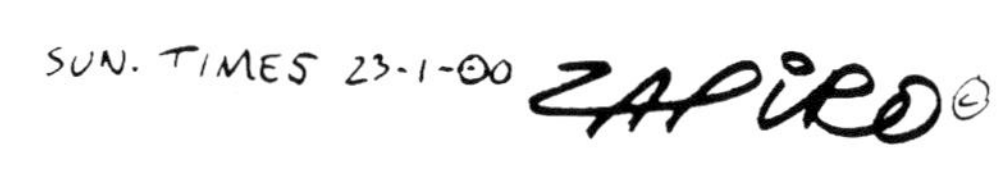

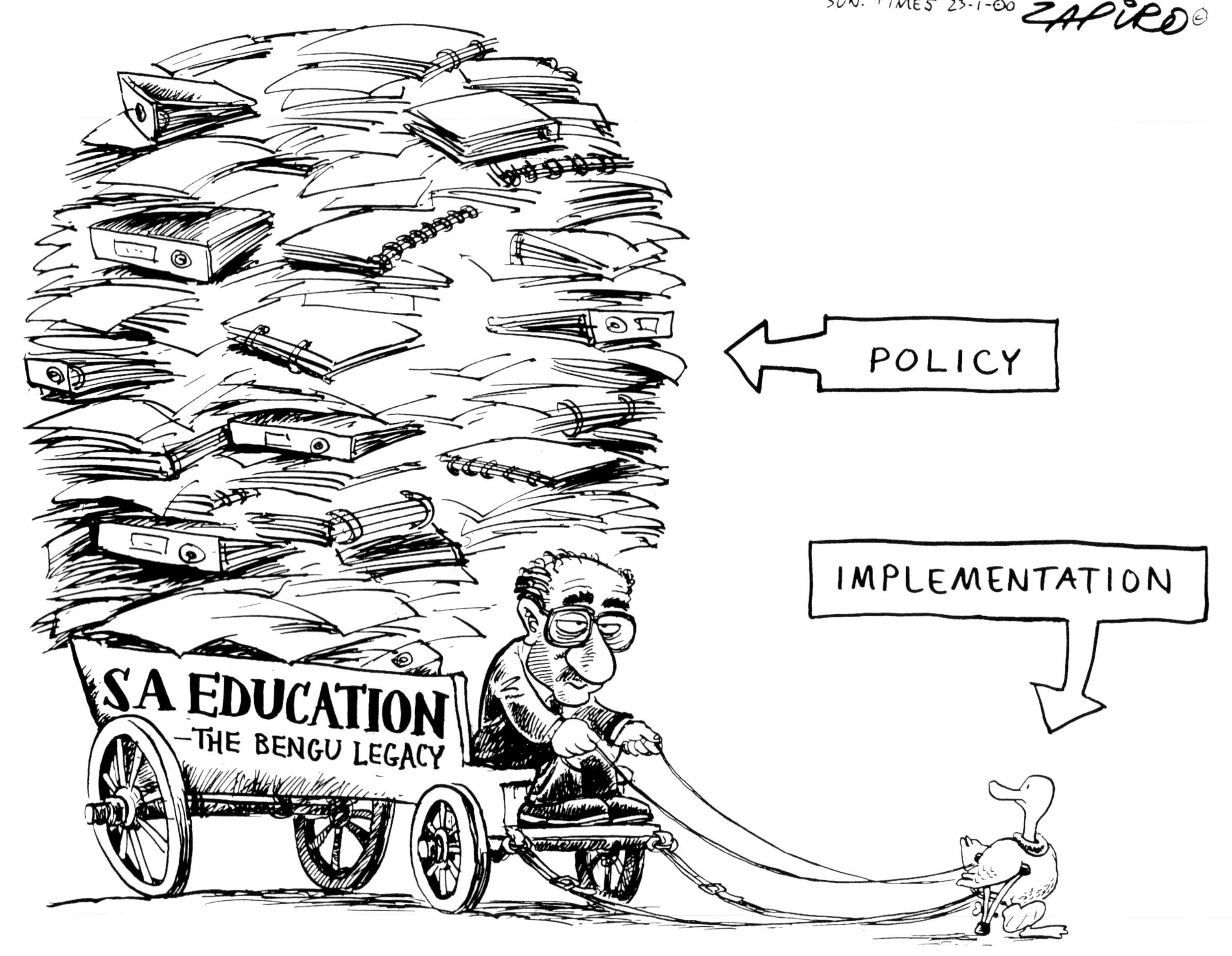

23 January 2000

27 January 2000

27 January 2000

Q. What do these people have in common?

A. They're all excluded from the government's brilliant new National AIDS Council.

3 February 2000

4 February 2000

10 February 2000

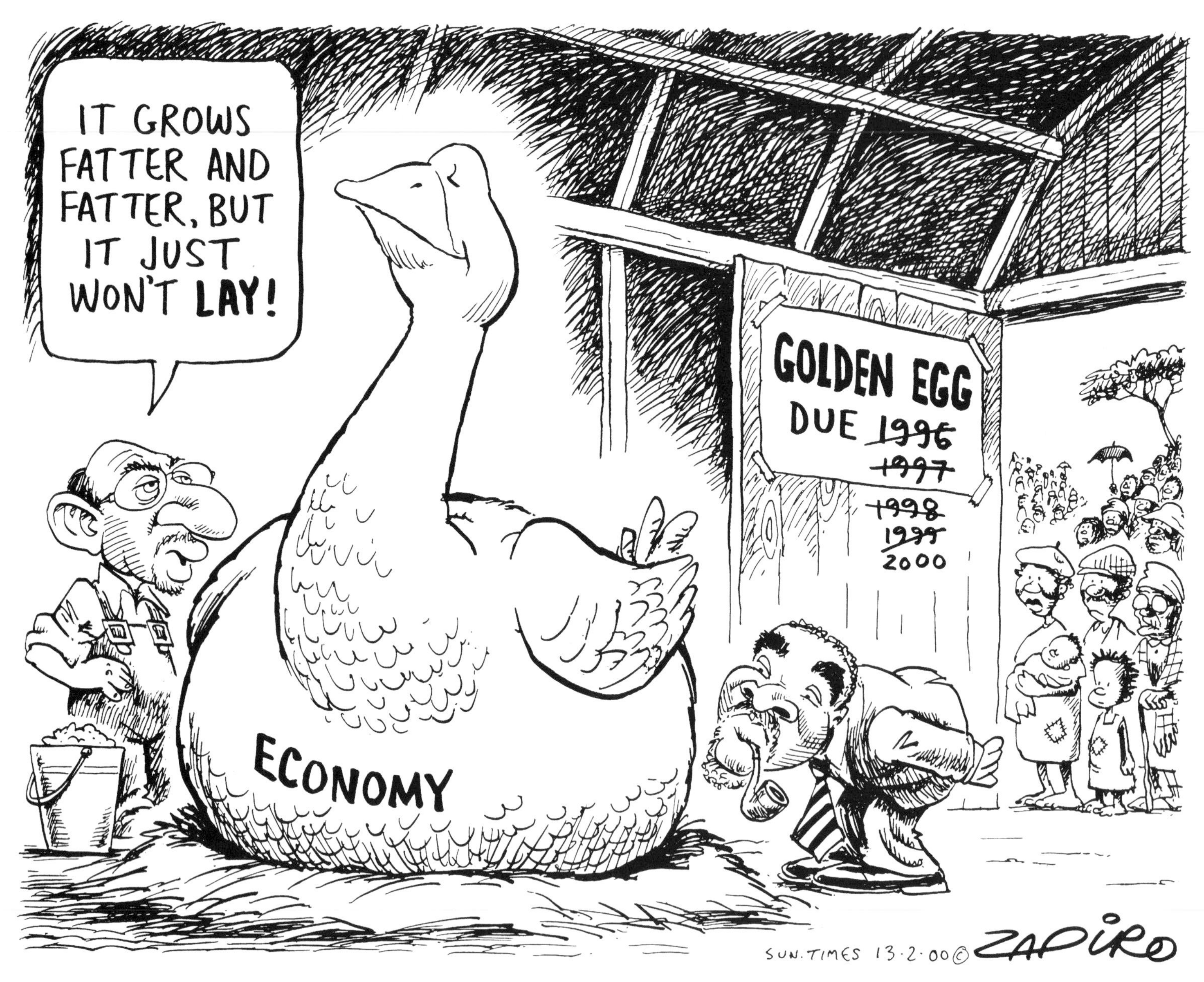

13 February 2000

20 February 2000 Mugabe's proposed constitutional amendments, designed to entrench his power, are rejected in a national referendum

22 February 2000

Massive floods in northern SA and neighbouring countries

23 February 2000

Instead of inviting the media to attend hearings into media racism, the Human Rights Commission issues subpoenas

17 February 2000

Armed with subpoenas and preconceptions

24 February 2000

27 February 2000 The Human Rights Commission mistakenly subpoenas London's *Financial Times*

SO WHAT'S TODAY'S SUBJECT?
THE HRC'S HEARINGS INTO RACISM IN THE MEDIA.

I'LL TRY TO SHOW THAT DESPITE STARTING EMBAR-RASSINGLY WITH THE BRAUDE REPORT, THE PROCESS SEEMS TO BE GOING WELL.
CLAUDIA
BARNEY

I SUPPORT THE BLACK EDITORS' VIEW THAT THE MEDIA IS STILL TOO WHITE-DOMINATED...
...ALTHOUGH THAT'S IRONIC COMING FROM A WHITEY CARTOONIST ON A BLACK NEWSPAPER!

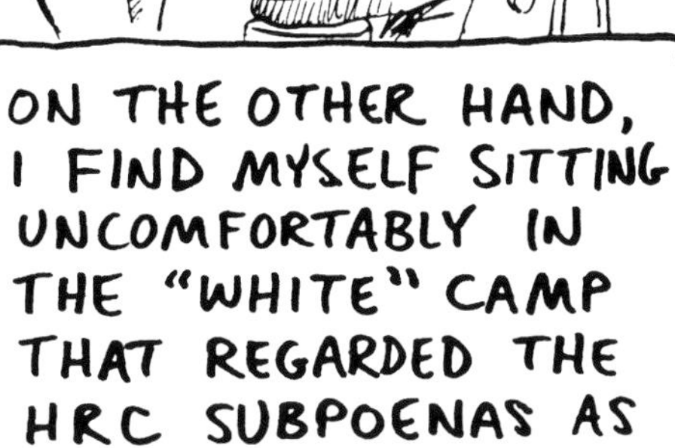
ON THE OTHER HAND, I FIND MYSELF SITTING UNCOMFORTABLY IN THE "WHITE" CAMP THAT REGARDED THE HRC SUBPOENAS AS A THREAT TO PRESS FREEDOM..

..WHILE I DISTANCE MYSELF FROM THOSE WHITE MEDIA PEOPLE WHO USED THE SUB-POENAS ISSUE TO AVOID HONEST DIS-CUSSION ABOUT RACISM.

I'D LIKE TO REFLECT ALL THESE COMPLEXITIES..

..IN ONE CARTOON IN TIME FOR MY 5 O'CLOCK DEADLINE.
GOOD LUCK.
SOWETAN 9-3-00 © ZAPIRO

9 March 2000

A chicken chain's TV commercial about a mischievous guide dog

2 March 2000

Nando's
Chickenland
STOP NANDO'S ADVERT
STOP NANDO'S ADVERT
STOP NANDO'S
SOWETAN 3.3.00 © ZAPIRO

3 March 2000

5 March 2000

Mozambican catastrophe

SA 2006 BID
WELCOMES
FIFA INSPECTION TEAM
ZE FACILITIES ARE IMPRESSIVE, BUT WHAT ABOUT ZE VIOLENCE?
DON'T WORRY, THAT'S JUST SAFA EXECUTIVES...
DANNY JORDAAN
M&G 9-3-00 ZAPIRO©

9 March 2000

16 March 2000

14 March 2000

16 March 2000

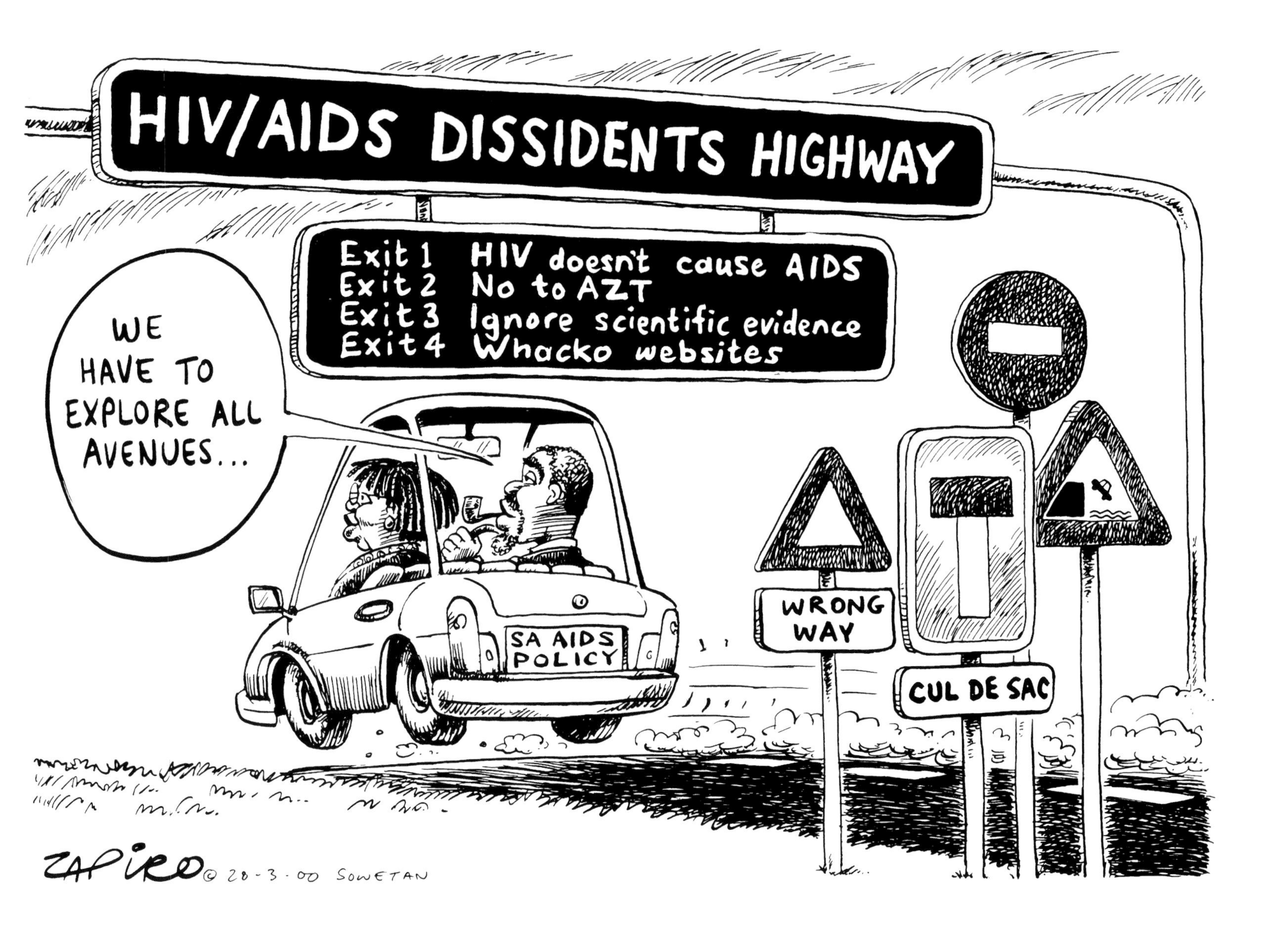

28 March 2000

The Crusades, the Inquisition etc. ...

23 March 2000

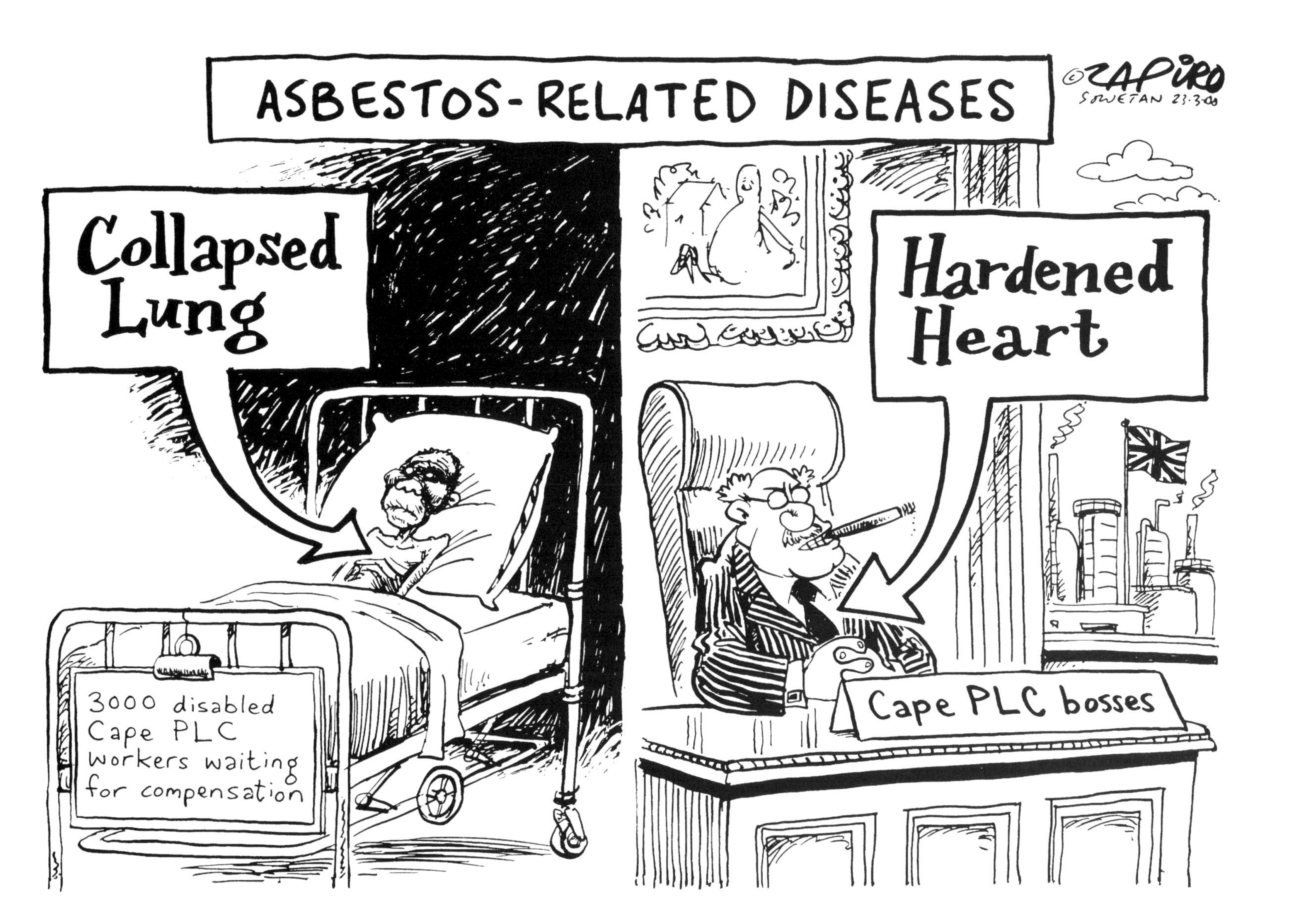

23 March 2000

26 March 2000

R200 million set aside last year for poverty relief is lying unspent

Eugene Terreblanche's one-year jail sentence for assault is upheld. And his six-year sentence for attempted murder is still on appeal.

30 March 2000

31 March 2000

In Ventersdorp prison

2 April 2000

Riddled with mismanagement, cliques and infighting

LINDELA TRANSIT CENTRE
NEXT ILLEGAL ALIEN DEPORTATION TO MOZAMBIQUE
I WAS CUTTING HAIR IN SOWETO...
I WAS A HAWKER IN HILLBROW...
I WAS HEAD OF SABC NEWS...
FORGED C.V.
ENOCH SITHOLE
4-4-00 SOWETAN
ZAPIRO

4 April 2000

?
EUROPE'S AGENDA
DEMOCRACY
AFRICA'S AGENDA
DEBT CANCELLATION
CAIRO WELCOMES
E.U. – O.A.U.
SUMMIT
ZAPIRO © SOWETAN 5·4·00

5 April 2000

ZAPIRO
© SOWETAN
6·4·00
B.C. AMALGAMATED
PAC
SOPA
AZAPO
JUST THINKING...

6 April 2000

11 April 2000 Police in India disclose a tape in which Hansie Cronje and a bookie are heard to be fixing a match. 'Absolute rubbish!' says Cronje.

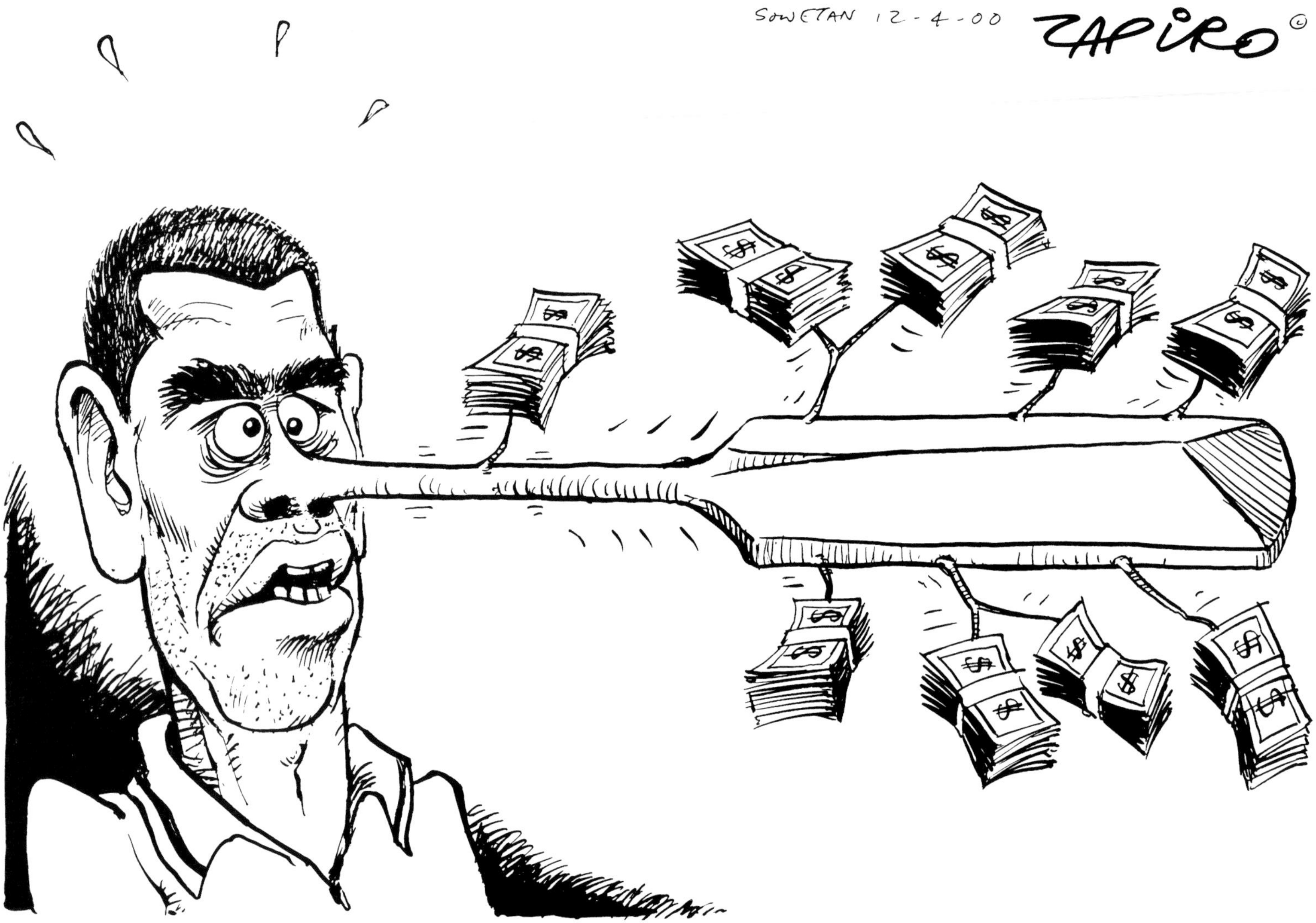

SOWETAN 12-4-00 ZAPIRO ©

12 April 2000 In a confession to Pastor Ray McCauley, Cronje admits he 'hasn't been completely honest' in his denials. He owns up to taking money for information, but still denies fixing matches.

13 April 2000

16 April 2000

20 April 2000

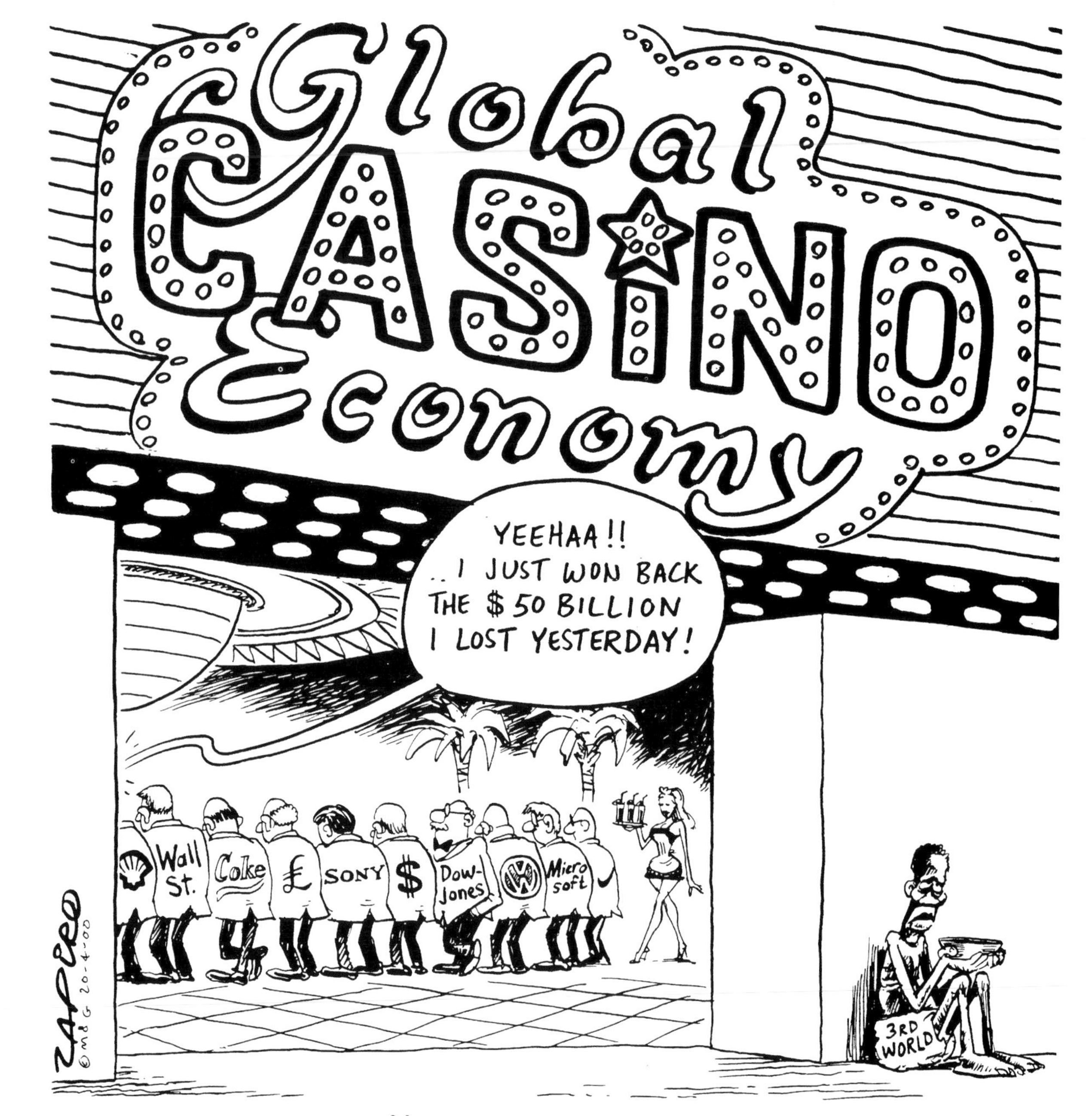

20 April 2000

19 April 2000

23 April 2000 With a national election in mind, Mugabe brands opposition parties as traitors and supports land invasions by self-styled 'war veterans'. Regional leaders are reluctant to criticize him.

ZIMBABWE TRADE FAIR
WELCOMES PRES. MBEKI
..AND HERE'S OUR VERY LATEST IN FARMING IMPLEMENTS...
PETROL
MATCHES
SUN. TIMES 7.5.00
ZAPIRO

7 May 2000

SOME ZIMBABWEAN POLITICAL PARTIES

25 May 2000

SA is ready to contribute a contingent to a UN peace initiative

4 May 2000

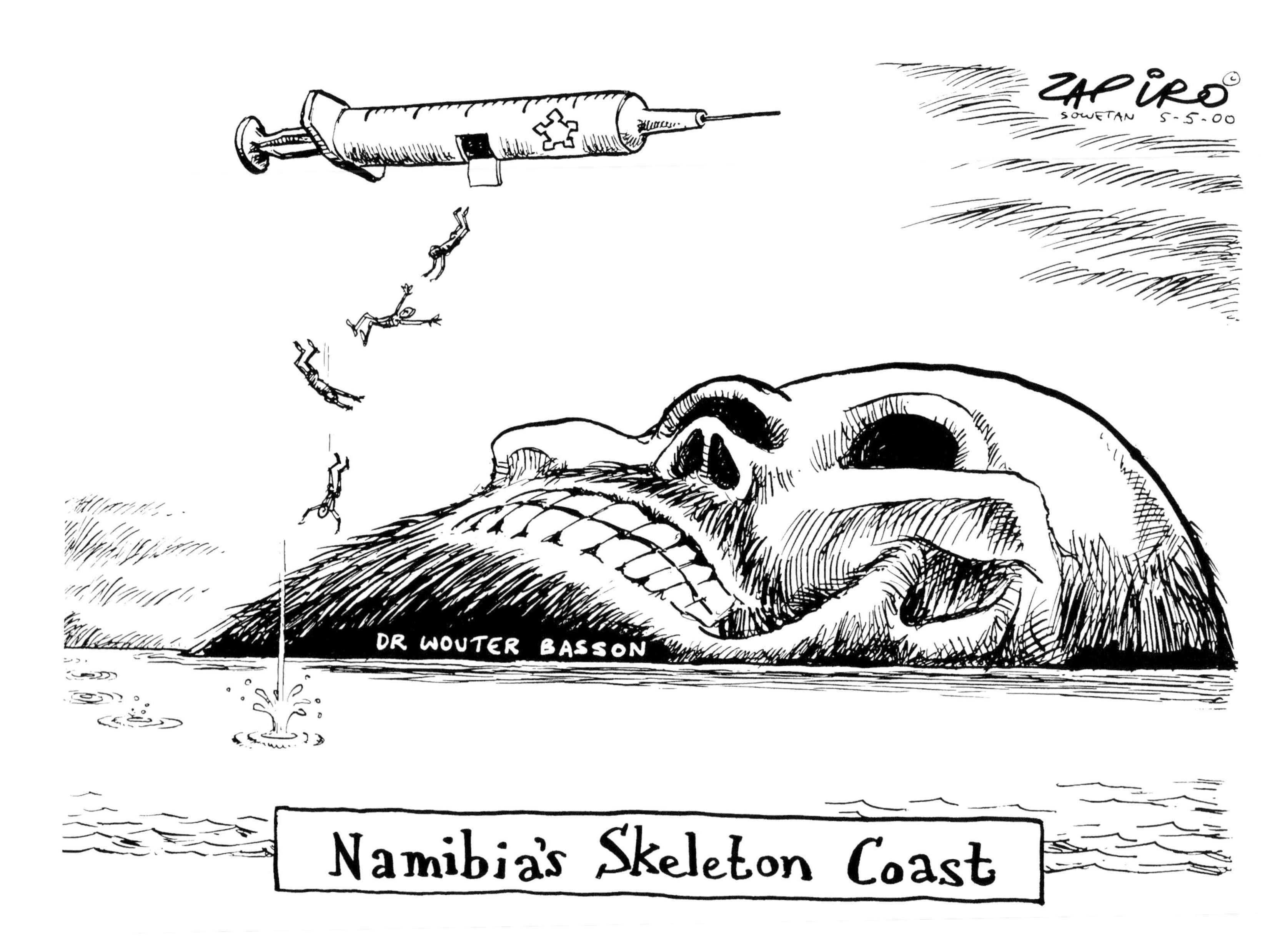

5 May 2000 Evidence in court that apartheid-era Namibian activists had been sedated with drugs supplied by Basson, and then thrown from aircraft to their deaths

Few details yet, but plenty of speculation

11 May 2000

12 May 2000

This week the joke became reality

14 May 2000

Allan Boesak gets a three-year sentence

ZAPIRO ©
M&G 18-5-00
CREW ONLY
BOGUS PILOTS BOUGHT LICENCES

18 May 2000

FODAY SANKOH'S BEEN CAPTURED!!
I'D DANCE AND CLAP HANDS, BUT....
SIERRA LEONE
WANTED
FODAY SANKOH
FOR A CAMPAIGN OF TERROR AND AMPUTATION
SOWETAN 19-5-00 © ZAPIRO

19 May 2000

A KISS ON THE CHEEK MAY BE CROSS-CONTINENTAL...
SAVIMBI
ANGOLA TREATY
SIERRA LEONE TREATY
FODAY SANKOH
...BUT DIAMONDS ARE A GUERILLA'S BEST FRIEND!
RRIP!
TREATY
RRIP!
TREATY
ANGOLAN DIAMOND FIELDS
SIERRA LEONE DIAMOND FIELDS
SUN. TIMES 21-5-00
ZAPIRO ©

21 May 2000

24 May 2000

On an American tour to seek investment

ZAPIRO
© SOWETAN 25-5-00
thanks ka
KAIZER CHIEFS
ORLANDO PIRATES
SPONSORED BY vodacom
KOO
KOO
OTHER
CLUBS
WHAT??
I SAID...: WHEN'LL A @#&* CELLPHONE COMPANY PUT R120 MILLION WHERE IT'S REALLY NEEDED?!!

25 May 2000

27 May 2000 A procession of witnesses with protected identities tell the court of bizarre 007-type poison gadgetry

I, ON THE OTHER HAND, CAN'T WAIT FOR THAT NEW GUN LAW!
"An Afrikaner's guns are second only to his wife." — CONSTAND VILJOEN (WHO OWNS 12)
30-5-00 SOWETAN ZAPIRO ©

30 May 2000

Welcome to
Marlboro Country.

31 May 2000

MR DELIVERY
ANNIVERSARY MONTH
PLEASE LEAVE YOUR ORDER AFTER THE BEEP... BEEP!
ARE YOU THERE?... WE'RE STILL WAITING FOR REPARATIONS, POVERTY RELIEF, JOB CREATION, LAND RESTITUTION....
MR DELIVERY
SOWETAN 2-6-00
ZAPIRO ©

2 June 2000

SIT!

LIE DOWN!

ROLL OVER!

FETCH!

ZAPIRO ©
SOWETAN 6-6-00
CRAIG WILLIAMSON

GOOD AMNESTY COMMITTEE!
AMNESTY
despite lack of full disclosure

6 June 2000

In China our Defence Minister cuts a deal

8 June 2000

9 June 2000 Although millions in reparation money are already available, politics prevents payment to the 20 000 victims identified by the TRC

4 June 2000 On the eve of the King Commission, a dramatic about-face by Cronje: yes, he *is* guilty of match-fixing and has involved other players, with a little help from a friend ...

MUNCH
MUNCH
GIBBS
WILLIAMS
SA CRICKET
SUN.TIMES 11·6·00
ZAPIRO ©

11 June 2000

THE BAD NEWS IS YOUR SON CHEATS, TELLS LIES AND BULLIES HIS PEERS INTO DOING BAD THINGS.
PRINCIPAL
THE GOOD NEWS IS HE COULD BECOME SOUTH AFRICA'S CRICKET CAPTAIN.
SOWETAN 12-6-00
© ZAPIRO

12 June 2000

YOU KNOW YOU'VE HIT ROCK BOTTOM WHEN YOU KEEP ON LOSING AND NO-ONE EVEN ACCUSES YOU OF MATCH-FIXING...
BAFANA BAFANA 0
OPPONENTS PLENTY
SOWETAN 13·6·00 ZAPIRO ©

13 June 2000

ANY FURTHER FINAL VERSIONS, MR CRONJE?
ADV. GAUNTLETT
JUDGE KING
M&G 14.6.00
© ZAPIRO

14 June 2000

I NEED A MOMENT TO CONSULT MY ADVISOR...
ZAPIRO ©
SOWETAN 21.6.00

21 June 2000

COME AND MEET SOME MORE NEW FRIENDS.
THAT'S IT!!.. ..I'M OUTTA HERE!
APARTHEID PETS
DP
LIBERAL PRINCIPLES
MANGOPE
KRIEL
TERTIUS DELPORT
GRRRR!!
18-6-00 SUN.TIMES
ZAPIRO ©

18 June 2000

20 June 2000 An opposition alliance is mooted. Despite the NNP's objections, it will be called the 'Democratic Alliance'.

GEAR
CRITICISM
CRIME
EDUC-ATION
REPAR-ATIONS
THABO'S HOT POTATOES
AIDS
ZIM
ZAPIRO © SOWETAN 19-6-00

19 June 2000

The UN withdraws its election monitors, citing gross irregularities

22 June 2000

FFICE OF THE PRESIDENT
SA
WITH THE ZIMBABWE ELECTION DAYS AWAY, HAS PRESIDENT MBEKI NOTED..

..WIDESPREAD INTIMIDATION BY ZANU PF SUPPORTERS...

..OPPOSITION GROUPS ATTACKED AND PREVENTED FROM CAMPAIGN-ING...

..JOURNALISTS BEATEN BY ZANU PF THUGS...

..THE UNCON-STITUTIONAL EMASCULATION OF ZIMBABWE'S ELECTORAL COMMISSION...

..HUNDREDS OF FOREIGN OBSERVERS BARRED...

...AND THE WITHDRAWAL OF U.N. MONITORS BECAUSE OF GROSS IRREG-ULARITIES?

YES, BUT APART FROM THAT, EVERY-THING'S ON TRACK.
ZAPIRO ©
22-6-00
SOWETAN

22 June 2000

SUN. TIMES 25-6-00 ZAPIRO©
FREE
AND
FAIR

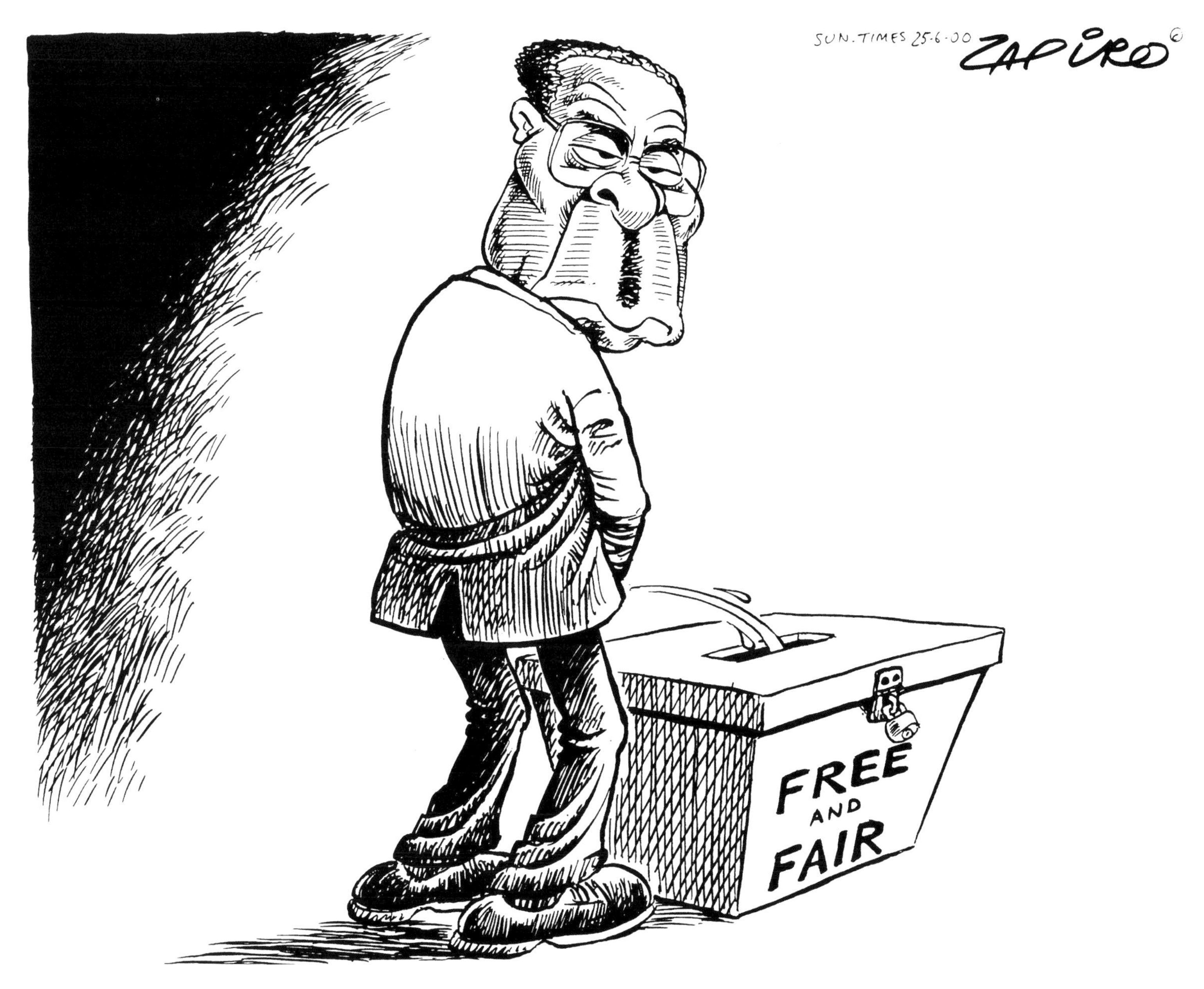

25 June 2000

29 June 2000 Unlike the campaign period, election weekend goes peacefully. Morgan Tsvangirai's Movement for Democratic Change does well, all things considered.

28 June 2000 The wreck of the *Treasure* leaves thousands of penguins oiled. Meanwhile the former NP Cabinet Minister receives a two-year sentence for stealing funds intended for the West Coast community.

CORRUPTION CORPORATION
OFFICIAL CORRUPTION CENTRE
DOCUFAKE
WE FAKE:
• I.D.s
• C.V.s
• DEGREES
• DRIVERS LICENCES
• PILOT'S LICENCES
One-stop Scam shop
CROOKERY BOOKS
FAST FRAUD
Match-Fixing Mall
MONEY LAUNDRY
BRIBERY BAR
RIP-OFF MART
CHOP SHOP
NO QUESTIONS
THE WORST THING IS EVENTUALLY IT ALL BECOMES NORMAL.
M&G 29-6-00 ZAPIRO ©

29 June 2000

5 July 2000

The host country for the 2006 World Cup is about to be announced

6 July 2000

The feeling is we can't lose

9 July 2000

We lose. By one vote.

10 July 2000 The New Zealander whose abstention from the FIFA vote flouted his country's mandate and cost us the bid

SOWETAN 4-7-00 ZAPIRO ©
WE NOTE WITH CONCERN THAT THE DURBAN AIDS DECLARATION HAS BEEN REJECTED BY THE HOST NATION'S HEALTH MINISTER.
WORLD AIDS CONFERENCE
AIDS SCIENCE

4 July 2000

President Mbeki's opening address is expected to acknowledge that HIV causes AIDS. Instead he says poverty is a major cause.

13 July 2000

13th WORLD AIDS CONFERENCE
THIS GATHERING CLOSES WITH CONSENSUS THAT THERE IS NO NEED FOR FURTHER DEBATE ON WHETHER HIV CAUSES AIDS.
AS WE AWAIT PRESIDENT MBEKI, A LONE PROTESTER IS LED AWAY...
WAIT! ..THAT **IS** PRESIDENT MBEKI!
SUN. TIMES 16-7-00 ZAPIRO ©

16 July 2000

13 July 2000 Deaths and injuries as someone targets Golden Arrow buses. Taxi bosses are the chief suspects.

M&G 20-7-00
ZAPIRO ©
BAM!!
BAM!!
BAM!!
CAPENEWS
20 BOMBS
60 BUS ATTACKS
NO CONVICTIONS
POLICE ARE LEAVING NO STONE UNTURNED, THE MINISTER SAID...

20 July 2000

19 July 2000

'War veterans' leader Chenjerai Hunzvi

HELP!
KEEP IT DOWN, WILL YOU?.. IT'S AGREED IN PRINCIPLE AND IMPLEMENTATION IS ON THE AGENDA FOR OUR NEXT MEETING.
G8
OKINAWA SUMMIT
AFRICA
DEBT RELIEF
..OR THE ONE AFTER THAT. ..IT DEPENDS...
ZAPIRO 23-7-00 © SUN.TIMES

23 July 2000

SOWETAN 24-7-00 ZAPIRO ©
PRETORIA TECHNIKON INVITES HANSIE CRONJE TO LECTURE IN ETHICS
PRETORIA TECHNIKON
LECTURER
COURSE OFFERED
P.W. Botha: Democracy
Parks Mankahlana: Parental Responsibility
Tony Leon: Affirmative Action Imperatives
Thabo Mbeki: Retroviral Science
Charlie Dempsey: Advancing the African Renaissance
*Allan Boesak: Advanced Accounting
*Abe Williams: Wealth Redistribution
*Eugene TerreBlanche: Race Relations
(* BY CORRESPONDENCE ONLY)

24 July 2000

IT FEELS LIKE WE'RE NOT EVEN PLAYING THE SAME TOUR AS TIGER...
BRITISH OPE
ZAPIRO © SOWETAN 25-7-00

25 July 2000

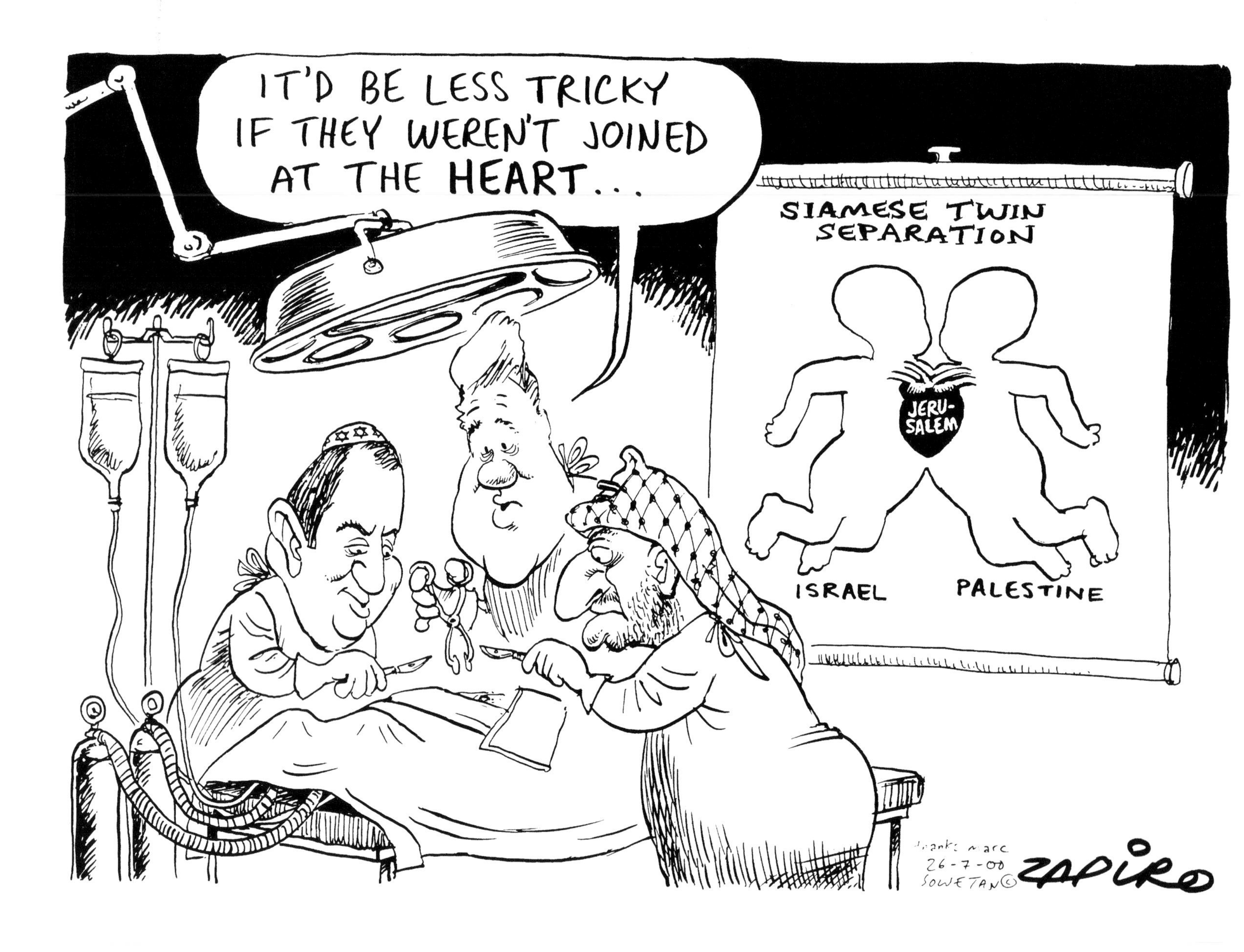

26 July 2000

Middle East peace talks at Camp David

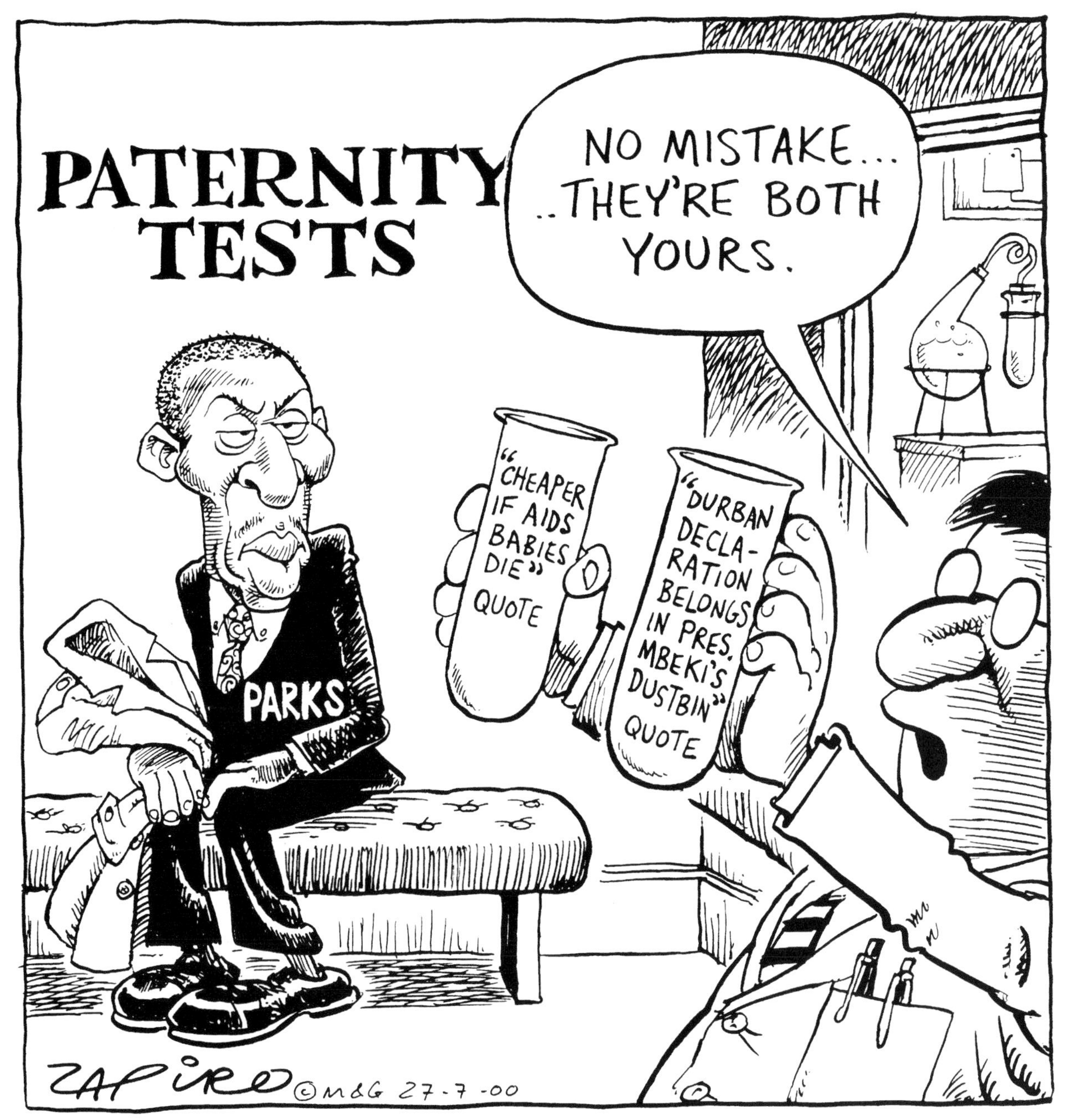

Presidential spokesperson Parks Mankahlana has recently made rash statements. He's also facing two child-maintenance suits.

27 July 2000

28 July 2000 Irvin Khoza and Danny Jordaan leave for Europe, aiming to take FIFA to arbitration over the 2006 voting procedure

KEEP GOING, DANNY! .. I THOUGHT I SAW SOME MOVEMENT!
..AND ZE VINNER ISS... ...DEUTSCHLAND!
IRVIN
SA 2006
SA 2006
SA 2006
MUNCH MUNCH
ZAPIRO 30-7-00 ©SUN TIMES

30 July 2000

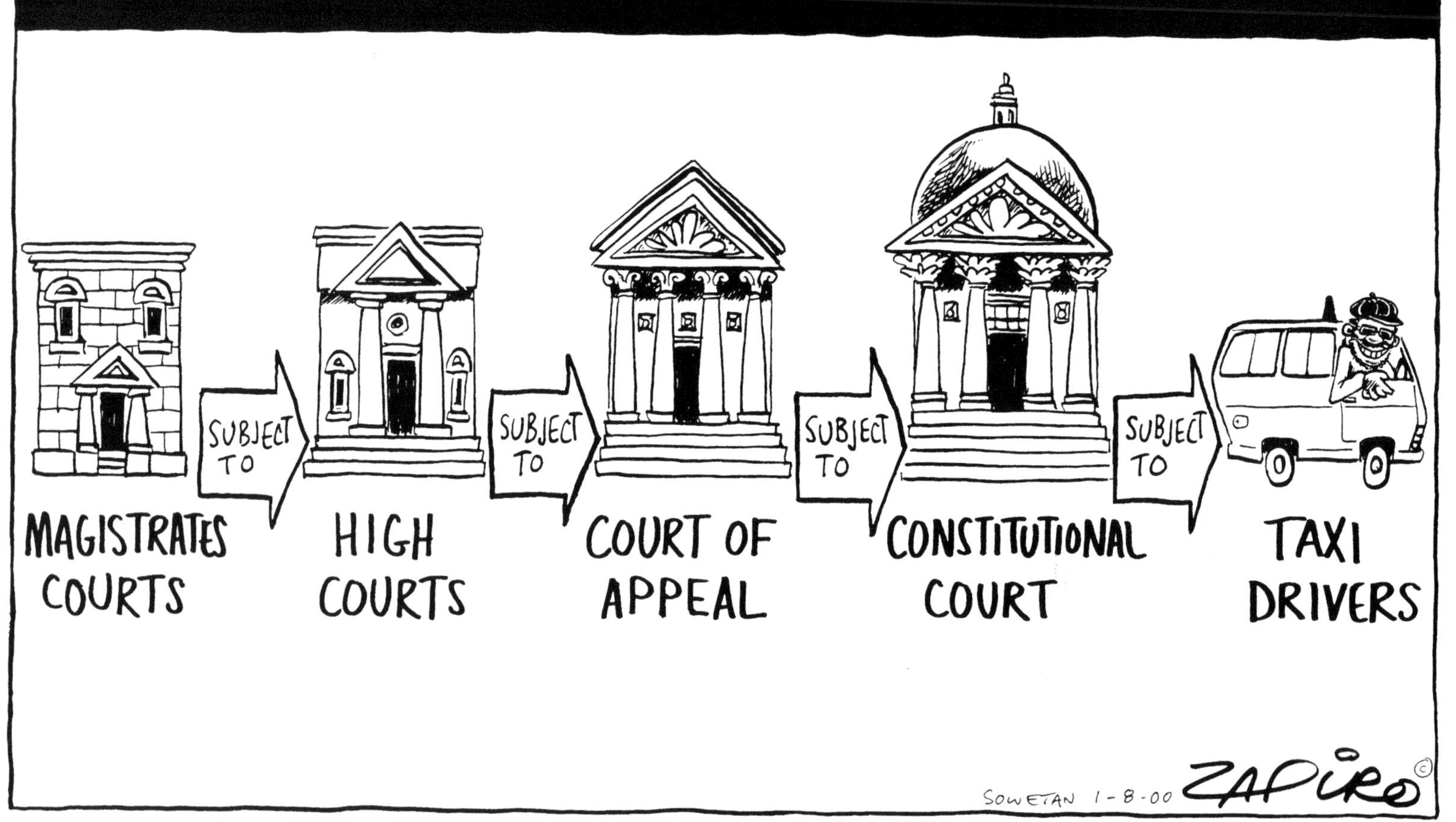

1 August 2000

Taxi wars, traffic violations, blockades …

Curriculum 2005 is impractical, Prof Asmal said months ago. Cabinet disagrees. He will implement it after all (with 'modifications').

3 August 2000

6 August 2000

The military admits to using journalists as intelligence sources

8 August 2000 It may be dubious and about to be shut down by the authorities, but it has hooked thousands of desperate investors

And it's all factual

10 August 2000

10 August 2000

13 August 2000

Complicated negotiations for the release of tourists captured months ago by Abu Sayaff guerillas

17 August 2000

THE GIANT TELESCOPE TO BE BUILT IN THE NORTHERN CAPE WILL BE THE MOST POWERFUL OF ITS KIND IN THE SOUTHERN HEMISPHERE...

..ALLOWING US TO VIEW SOME OF THE MOST DISTANT OBJECTS IN THE UNIVERSE.

17 August 2000

16 August 2000 President Mbeki attributes Tony Leon's criticism of his eccentric AIDS stance to racism

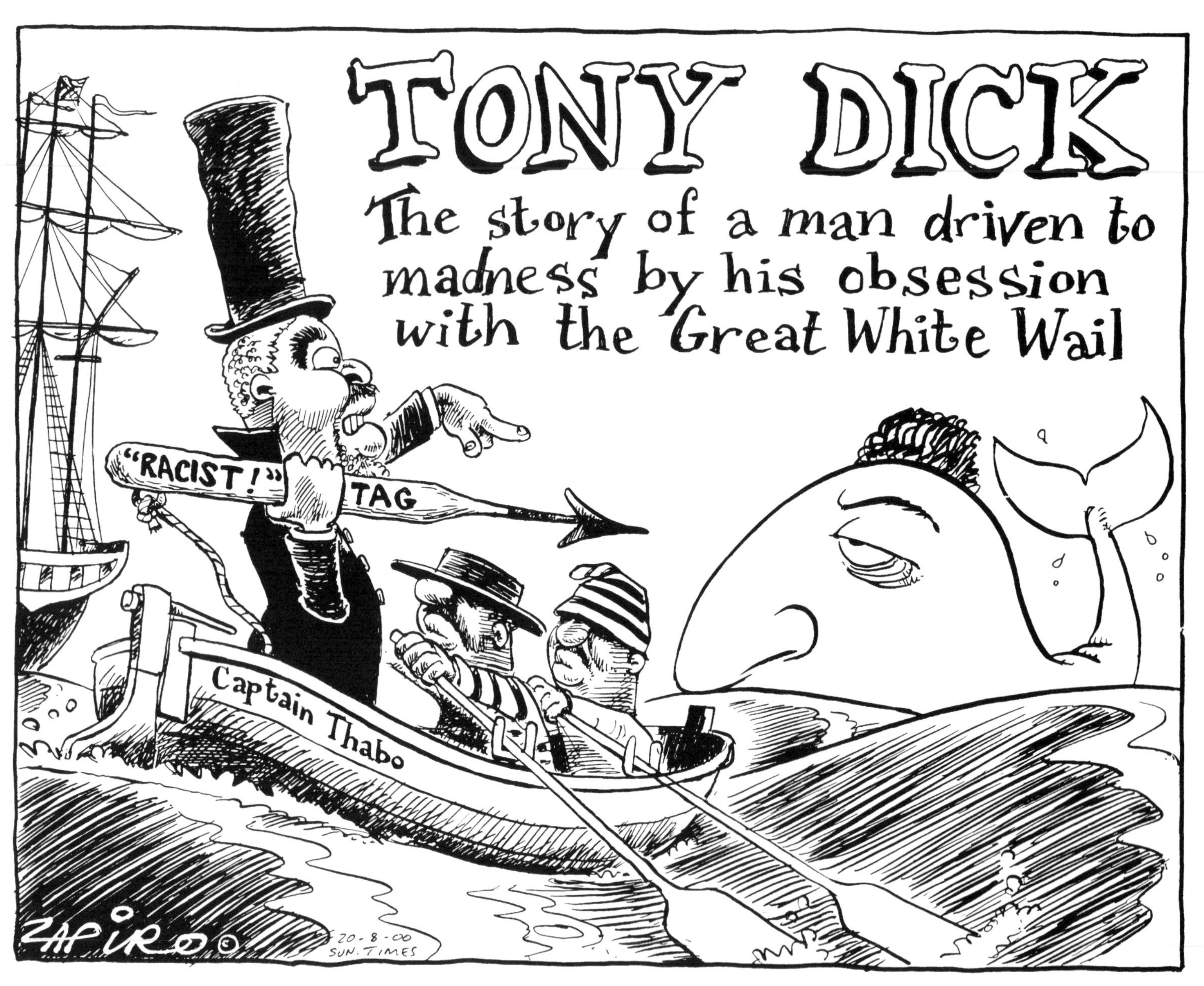

20 August 2000

Existing gun control, SA

22 August 2000

As the Firearms Control Bill is debated

23 August 2000 An explosion cripples the *Kursk*. Pride prevents Russia's top brass from allowing foreign teams to help rescue efforts until it is too late to save any of the 118 crew members.

27 August 2000

The HRC's jargon-filled report into racism in the media damns even progressive media as racist

24 August 2000

25 August 2000 Black frustration and white denial ahead of the HRC's hearings into racism (which will be more successful than their media racism hearings)

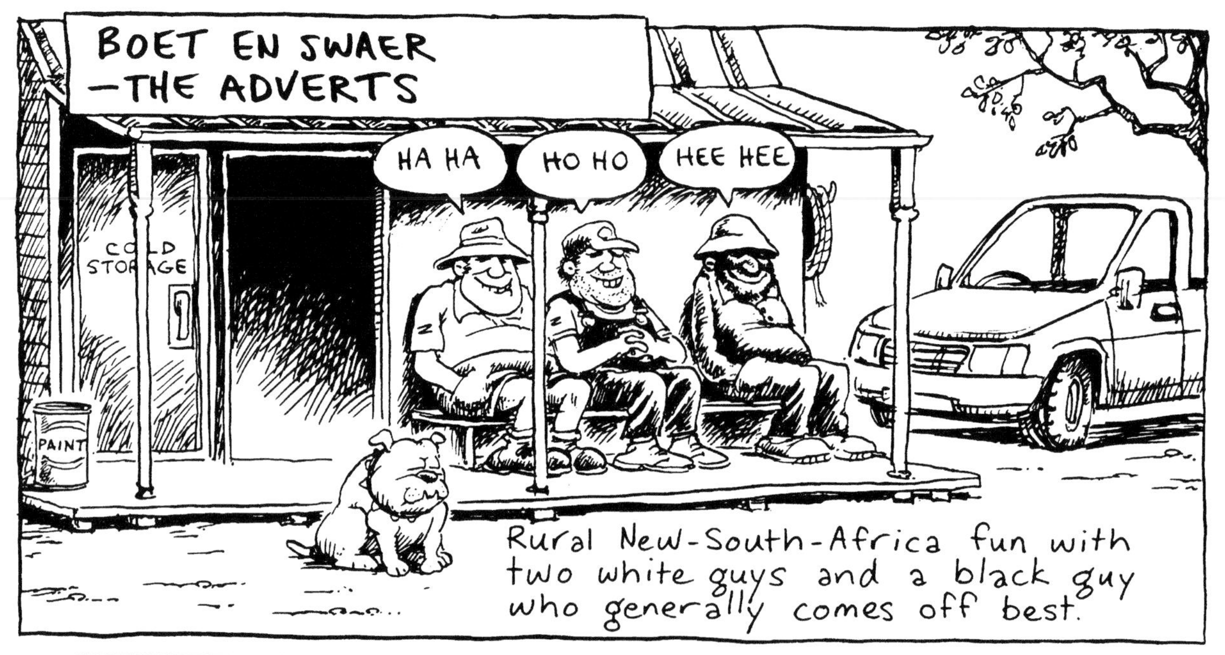

31 August 2000

WHITES WHO NEVER BENEFITTED FROM APARTHEID:

5 September 2000

31 August 2000 Gaddafi's intervention secures the release from Jolo Island of the Abu Sayaff movement's foreign hostages

3 September 2000

THAT ONE'S FROM SOUTH AFRICA...
ZAPIRO 2.7.00 © SUN.TIMES

2 July 2000